Bus Stop Bus Stop

Bus Stop Bus Stop

Grant Guy

Bus Stop Bus Stop
© 2017 Grant Guy

ISBN-13:978-1-970003-08-6

Cover Artwork © 2017 Shawn Jordan
Cover design © Red Dashboard LLC

Red Dashboard LLC Publishing
Princeton NJ 08540
Red Dashboard Press Windsor
Ontario, Canada
www.reddashboard.com

To all that have loved
and lost to love again.

And to Di Brandt for her editorial advice.

The floors of bus stations are the same all over the country, always covered with butts and spit and they give a feeling of sadness that only bus stations have.

Jack Kerouac, On the Road.
Penguin Modern Classics, 2011

FORWARD

 I recall watching a documentary on the British director Peter Brook. In the documentary he was talking about his travels. He was asked if he preferred to make theatre or travel (or something close to that. I often remember things as I want to remember them.). He answered he preferred to travel but he had to make theatre to afford to travel (again, something like that).

I have worked most of my adult life in theatre. At first I made theatre because I liked the art form, and the more I made theatre the more travelling I was required to do. I usually took the train or bus because I have a fear of flying (I do take planes but trains remain my preferred means of travel.), and, in doing so, I discovered I liked ground transportation because of the fleeting friendships that were made. The revelation of secrets.

Something happens on trains and buses that did not occur in planes (besides the Mile High Club). That something is the train and bus becomes a rolling confessional. People un-costume their personality, stripping off the public self in favor of the private self. They do this because, in all likelihood, they will never see you again.

It is a liberating experience, cathartic, purgation. Respite comes through a release. For 36 or 48 hours they have redemption.

And there are the little and big dramas of life happening all around you on trains and buses. You witness human nobility and human despair. Through the isolation of the train or bus, and for 36 or 48 hours, you are exempt from the world. It is a little Eugene Ionesco and a little Jean-Paul Sartre.

Our bus stopped in Odessa, Texas, for a bathroom break and to grab a coffee perhaps. The line-up to the washrooms was long. Some passengers walked over to a McDonald's some one hundred yards away.

Soon the bus was prepared to go. The driver counted the passengers, climbed behind the wheel and began to pull away. I knew he had left someone behind. You could ignore some passengers, but the Amish passenger was not easy to ignore. The missing passenger's Amish travelling companion sat passively. I went to the driver to tell him he had left a passenger behind. He insisted everyone was counted for. The bus continued to pull away as I pointed to the Amish passenger hurrying out of McDonald's to catch the bus.

The driver said, "Well, if he is left behind he can use the phone and call for help."
"He's Amish!" I said.
"What has that got to do with it?" answered the driver.

Ionesco in Sartre's NO EXIT.

BUS 1218

Maybe it's due to a chemical disorder, but I like transcontinental buses.

On buses, I find each psychopath unrepeatable. They instill in me fear. They give me new glimpses into the world through unaltered lenses. They give me stories.

The same goes for each Cree or Ojibway grandfather and grandmother travelling only a hundred miles down the road, and the truck driver going as far as Dryden to pick up a rig to return it to Thunder Bay.

And the same goes for the couple making out at the back of the bus. I only pray they keep it under the blanket.

BUS 3384

There is a warm-blanket-comfort driving at night.

In the light of the day people drive from A to B as if there is
nothing special in it. There is an inhumane loneliness
inherent in daytime driving. B is just a destination without
poetry. But travelling an interstate, enveloped by the night,
brings out all that is magical about the road. In us.

The music on your stereo system has a resonance that
vanishes in the light of day. The music at night is direct, and
not lost to the droning hum of the tires and engine. At night
the engine purrs.

Talk radio becomes a Lenny Bruce concert. Under Milk
Wood. Charles Bukowski.

Truck drivers are the shepherds and guardian angels of the
highway. They lead us safely through fog and rain. Cut us
paths on snow-blown roads.

And the truck stop at night becomes a community center. It
welcomes with fluorescent hugs. Travelling alone at 3:00

p.m. we feel our loneliness. At 3:00 a.m., although we are strangers, we are with a community of friends we have known forever.

At 3:00 p.m. the waitress serves stale coffee. And at 3:00 a.m. the waitress with the coffee pot in her hand is our sister, our lover, and our friend.

The passengers that stumble out of the Greyhound at 3 a.m. with their zombie faces, cry and reach out, mumbling:
    "Coffee. Coffee."
The passengers will not get any sleep.

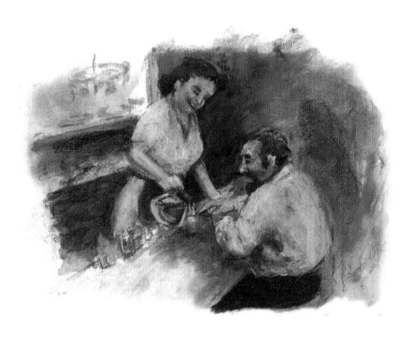

The unshaven man at the grill is that uncle no one talks about. He smells of bacon and cigarettes. His nicotine hands make the best burgers in Erie, Pennsylvania.

The gas jockey has a different aphorism for each fill up. And a nickname for each driver that he shares with only the nighthawks.

We have entered into that special world, and the time we spend with waitresses, with long-haul drivers, the highway patrol, the hitchhikers, the insomniacs, the drunks and addicts, and with the nocturnal scavengers is our secret society.

We are home.

BUS 2987

I travelled to LA to conduct a study tour of Cirque du Soleil. When I arrived at the bus depot in LA from Winnipeg in 1989, many people, more than I could count, were awaiting my arrival. They were waving, trying to get my attention.

"Me, me, me!" they cried out.

They made me feel like I was a Hollywood star: admired and worshipped.

My bus was three hours late arriving in LA. It was past midnight. I was too tired to make a selection as to which one I would choose. I did not want to hurt any of their feelings. Then I heard a deep voice behind me.

"They only want your money, man. They don't really care about you. None of them will treat you properly, dig? But my car service will get you anywhere you want. Where is it you want to go?"

"Santa Monica," I answered.

"Twenty dollars," he said. "I'll take you there for twenty dollars. The cabs will cost you twice as much, and all their cabs smell like shit."

I let him take my bag and he led me to his black Buick. I was tired. I could have easily fallen asleep, but his radio piped the sounds from a local jazz station. I relaxed as I listened to Coltrane, Davis, Lloyd and Parker.

BUS 2389

Returning home, I took the Greyhound from New York to Toronto. Drivers were exchanged in Buffalo. The stop allowed the passengers to stretch their legs.

I was standing outside the depot, smoking a Camel, when a tall man approached me.

He asked, "If you take this package across the border for me, there's $20 in it for you."

I looked at the package, tucked under his arm, and answered, "I've been in the joint a couple of times, and I have no desire to go back."

He released a soft, breathy huff.

"That's why I need someone to take the package across. What were you in for?"

"Armed robbery and conspiracy to commit."

I was lying through my nicotine teeth. Other than a brief stay as a vagrant, I'd never seen the inside of a prison.

"Served my time at Stony Mountain," I continued to lie.

The tall man was about to say something when he saw a teenager come out of the depot for a smoke. He walked over to the teenager and asked the kid the same question he'd asked me. The tall man handed the kid the package, followed by a $20 dollar bill. Then the tall man went inside the depot. The teenager, with the package gripped in his hand, took a drag on his cigarette.

The announcement, "The bus for Toronto is now boarding," was almost swallowed up by the sparse emptiness of the depot. The kid, the tall man, and I, along with all the other passengers, boarded the bus and took our seats.

At the Canadian border we exited the bus, took our luggage and lined up at customs. The kid exited the bus ahead of the tall man and me. The customs officers asked to see the package. A discussion ensued between the kid and the customs officers. By now the passengers were leaning forward to hear what was being said. An officer came around the long table, took the kid by the elbow and led him away. Through the window of an adjoining room we could see another customs officer opening the package.

The luggage of the passengers was quickly inspected.

Within 25 minutes everyone was back aboard the bus, except the driver and the kid. We sat on the idle bus until an officer boarded and took the tall man away.

It was another 20 minutes before the tall man and the driver climbed on board. As soon as the tall man was seated, the driver started up the bus, and it pulled away.

The tall man sat just across aisle from me. He never said a word until we reached Toronto. He just stared sullenly into the lightless window, seeing only his own reflection looking back, broken up by the headlights of vehicles heading south.

BUS 2389

Returning home, I took the Greyhound from New York to Toronto. Drivers were exchanged in Buffalo. The stop allowed the passengers to stretch their legs.

I was standing outside the depot, smoking a Camel, when a tall man approached me.

He asked, "If you take this package across the border for me, there's $20 in it for you."

I looked at the package, tucked under his arm, and answered, "I've been in the joint a couple of times, and I have no desire to go back."

He released a soft, breathy huff.

"That's why I need someone to take the package across. What were you in for?"

"Armed robbery and conspiracy to commit."

I was lying through my nicotine teeth. Other than a brief stay as a vagrant, I'd never seen the inside of a prison.

"Served my time at Stony Mountain," I continued to lie.

The tall man was about to say something when he saw a teenager come out of the depot for a smoke. He walked over to the teenager and asked the kid the same question he'd asked me. The tall man handed the kid the package, followed by a $20 dollar bill. Then the tall man went inside the depot. The teenager, with the package gripped in his hand, took a drag on his cigarette.

The announcement, "The bus for Toronto is now boarding," was almost swallowed up by the sparse emptiness of the depot. The kid, the tall man, and I, along with all the other passengers, boarded the bus and took our seats.

At the Canadian border we exited the bus, took our luggage and lined up at customs. The kid exited the bus ahead of the tall man and me. The customs officers asked to see the package. A discussion ensued between the kid and the customs officers. By now the passengers were leaning forward to hear what was being said. An officer came around the long table, took the kid by the elbow and led him away. Through the window of an adjoining room we could see another customs officer opening the package.

The luggage of the passengers was quickly inspected.

Within 25 minutes everyone was back aboard the bus, except the driver and the kid. We sat on the idle bus until an officer boarded and took the tall man away.

It was another 20 minutes before the tall man and the driver climbed on board. As soon as the tall man was seated, the driver started up the bus, and it pulled away.

The tall man sat just across aisle from me. He never said a word until we reached Toronto. He just stared sullenly into the lightless window, seeing only his own reflection looking back, broken up by the headlights of vehicles heading south.

BUS 4517

The further one travels south by train, automobile or bus, the more one sees the transition from a car culture to a bus culture.

The bus from Winnipeg south begins with a mere handful of passengers; four, five or six. But as it travels down the 29 to Sioux Falls and Sioux City more get on than off. From Omaha to Kansas City the number of onboard passengers increases substantially.

By the time we reach Dallas we are in the heart of the bus culture.

In the depot, passengers are crammed together. The depot is far too small for such an influx. We need to shoulder our way everywhere once inside. It takes brute force to navigate to the food and drink vending machines, but once there I have lost my appetite. What I saw in the public washrooms seemed almost more appealing, if it weren't for the junkies and overflowing toilets spilling human excrement onto the broken tile floor. However, Dallas is a florist shop compared to San Antonio.

Most buses departing Dallas, east to Florida or west to Los Angeles, are twinned with a second bus to handle the huge numbers of passengers. More buses and drivers are on standby. Each time I transferred buses in Dallas I was always seated on a standby bus.

You cannot smoke inside the depot. You need to step out onto the street, but be prepared for violence. Once, when I stepped out for my cigarette, I witnessed two cab drivers go at it over a disputed fare. Knives were drawn. What ended the violence was a third cab driver who drew a gun, and ordered both of them to back down.

The passenger in question was removed from one of the two taxis and shown into the third.

When the cops arrived they spoke to the driver with the gun before speaking to the two with the knives. Within ten minutes the cops were on their way. Guns and knives once more out of sight.

BUS 6645

The bus slid out of its berth at the Kansas City depot. Some passengers prayed while others simply kissed their asses goodbye. In a few hours we will be arriving in Dallas; then only God knows what will happen. Will any of us live to see

San Antonio or Laredo?

An addict with a plastic knife may have slipped through the metal detector. A disgruntled baggage handler may have brought a gun to work. Bryan Grant might be the focus of his rage, but he seems hell-bent on making sure Grant does not go alone into the void.

If the addict with the plastic knife had not worked up his courage, or the luggage handler's hour had not come before the bus left Dallas, the passengers wouldn't have left Dallas hungry. That sugary donut bought in Ardmore, Oklahoma, would have to suffice for another 6 or 7 of hours because the fruit and sandwiches in the vending machines were an abstract Composition in Green, Blue, White and Black.

The three-hour layover would feel like three weeks as the passengers clutched their purses and knapsacks to their chests. Money would be tucked away in money belts under their clothing. Those that could find a wall to lean their backs against would shiver with mortal dread. Their eyes would glance to the clock above the luggage lockers, as every second seemed to be grinding to a dead halt.

It would only be a few hours to Laredo. If there were a god those who had been praying to it would by now be cursing their choice of deity.

BUS 5972

Sitting next to me was an ironworker who wanted to be a poet. He showed me some of his poems. They were all about working people, blue-collar people. A few were actually very good. He said he had modest success in getting some of his poems published here and there. He said he had been rejected by all the major poetry journals, which, to his mind, were the private reserve of the academics. The Ojibway woman in the seat in front of him was telling the Anglican minister of her grandson's suicide. The minister admitted his words had lost all meaning, his words had done nothing to prevent the suicide of the young man. He was in doubt of his calling.

Across the aisle, a man in his mid-twenties, was telling the sixteen-year old girl how some day he was going to kill the Prime Minister. She looked like she was interested in what he was talking about, but it is hard to tell what the sixteen-year old girl was thinking, except she had a hand on his thigh.

Behind me were two women from Marathon travelling to

Wawa for a wedding. They were both in their thirties, but looking closer to fifty. Heavy drinking, heavy smoking, heavy eating and unhappy lives contributed to their defeated appearances.

At the back of the bus two young men, maybe nineteen or twenty, grumbled about the driver. He had already warned them about smoking in the washroom at the back of the bus. The driver had threatened to kick them off the bus if he caught them again.

A wife, who had been seen off by her husband in Dryden,

had already run the bases twice with the short order travelling to Saulte Ste. Marie, where he will be met by his wife.

In the first set of seats by the door was a retired couple on their way from Vancouver to Toronto, to visit their grandson. Except to ask for the salt or pepper to be passed at the meal breaks, they never spoke.

Across the aisle from them, sitting directly behind the driver, was a man who smiled a lot and rocked.

A broken-down wanna-be cowboy was travelling home to Nova Scotia after losing his job in the oil patch in Alberta. He was a very bitter man.

The old Saskatchewan CCFer was living theatre. He was not happy with today's NDP. He had only marginal interest in the Waffle.

"The only hard work they ever did was to turn the page of a book. The Waffle talked a lot about life but never lived it."

At each stop he paid for someone's coffee.

The driver spoke often on his cell phone.

A 7-Up can rolled around on the floor. No one bothered to pick it up.

The Greyhound moved into the night where its real seething poetry begins. Up to now everything had been merely prosaic.

The bus's headlights cut our path through the cave of darkness.

BUS 2858

I wish I remembered his name. I have also forgotten the name of the county in South Dakota he had served in as sheriff. All I am certain of is that it was in the middle of the state, but that could be either the counties of Potter, Dewey or Jackson.

I met him on a bus from Denver to Watertown, SD. At first he sat behind me. Later, on a regional line, he sat across the aisle. We had coffee together and took our meals together. He and his wife were returning home after visiting a daughter who taught elementary school in Denver.

He met none of my preconceived notions of a small town sheriff: overweight, prejudicial, mean spirited, an Old Testament Christian who never opened a Bible, and dumb as a fence post. He was as refreshing as the golden sun in the morning. He was tall, over six feet. He was well read and informed of the current events outside of the United States. Maybe there was a bit of Sheriff Taylor in him. When he could he fished with his sons and grandchildren.
And he never carried a gun. He thought carrying a gun

35

would be an invitation for someone to shoot him.

He carried out his duties in a green GMC pickup. He had a county sheriff van to transfer prisoners. For the first two decades as sheriff his wife, or Tommy Cowan, a local handyman, were the nearest people he had to deputies when transferring prisoners. On occasion his oldest boy took on that duty during the summer months.

He pissed-off his oldest boy when the kid was sixteen. The sheriff ticketed his son for drag racing with his buddies on a county road. The son thought his old man should have gone easy on him, but the sheriff believed all were equal under the law and all should be treated the same. He did not want his office to be tainted by any whiff of corruption. The sheriff saw too many rich and powerful in his county, in his state, and in his country, who abused their offices and positions to do favors for their own kind.

He'd been elected as sheriff as an independent. This was not by choice, but by the time he'd decided to run for the office of sheriff the primaries had closed. After winning, he thought about running on the Democratic Party ticket, but decided to stay independent. After seeing up close those elected to councils and boards, he noted how they became agents of their parties rather than representatives of the people.

For the first couple decades as sheriff he had a small office in the county seat administrative building, but his home was the office away from the office. He had a private phone line installed for police work, with an extension phone on the floor beside his bed. His wife joked,

"There were times I heard bells go off."

He had no dispatcher until 2001 when he hired Dee Dee as dispatcher, but most people in the county still called his police number at his house anyway. Dee Dee knitted

sweaters, scarves and socks for her grandchildren.

Instead of listening to rock or country music his children grew up with the constant chatter of the police radio. To hear their teenage music they had to go to Billy's for The Clash. Trudy's for Bon Jovi.

Many meals were shared with highway patrol officers passing by. Many times firefighters had a hot cup of coffee or cocoa after dousing a blaze.

On hot days the sheriff could be seen delivering lemonade to migrant farmhands out on the Wilson's or the Huxton's farms, or at the Eggland dairy.

Occasionally he would have to arrest someone who had become violent, but he found his gift of the gab (something he thought he inherited from his Irish grandmother) could defuse most such situations. He never fired a gun in 24 years.

He thought he might try and stay in office for another 20. He liked the job. He liked the people he served. It was the only job he really knew. His father was a deputy sheriff and US

Marshall. His two grandfathers were sheriffs and deputy sheriffs. His father-in-law was a highway patrol officer and sheriff.

The job had become a little easier since he'd hired a deputy. His wife thought he should have done it sooner.

"His job was our life," said his wife. "But we were a family."

The trip to Denver was their first get-away in a decade. A couple of years after being elected sheriff, he and his young family drove to White River to spend the day with his wife's side for Christmas. They had just arrived and he received a call about a plane-crash back home.

"We came back and never went away for a holiday again. That was 10 years ago", said his wife.

"If you really, really care about people, it isn't quite so hard, because you know them as friends," he said.

But he did say the hardest part of the job was when justice and the law came into conflict. He was a man of the law, had to enforce the law, but whenever he could he would try to persuade the law to see things from justice's point of view.

A year ago I stopped in Pier, SD, for the night. At supper I read a Pier newspaper with an article about the sheriff. He had retired after thirty-three years in office. He was going fishing.

BUS 2492

The day had folded into night as the bus pulled into Barstow.
It was there he boarded the bus. He was the last to get on.
Next to me was the only vacant seat. He had a small build,
but he squished his butt around enough in the seat to push
me against the wall. He was wearing a dirty white t-shirt,
jean jacket, jeans and sneakers. His long, streaky, blonde
hair matched his clothing.

41

He was quiet for a while, then, he asked where I was traveling to.

"Canada."

"I never met a fookin' Canadian before," he said.

From there he decided to share with me his "autobiography". That's what he called his life. An autobiography. He had been working as a laborer on a construction job outside of Barstow, but he'd been fired. He'd been caught balling a prostitute in the cab of a company truck. He had made matters worse by pulling a knife on a company security guard.

"I could've sliced the bastards fookin' throat." And then he added

"I'm going home to Arkansas. The first thing I'm gonna do when I get home is put my wife's fookin' face through the fookin' window of our fookin' trailer. The bitch's been sleeping around behind my fookin' back. She'll be lucky if I let her live."

He had the aforementioned knife straddled across his lap as he spoke, and kept it there. I did not sleep well that night. I thought of reporting him to the driver but my experience with transcontinental bus drivers told me they were not reliable or empathetic. They preferred to avoid trouble.

I witnessed an entire neighborhood avoid trouble. I stopped a murder in Minneapolis. Neighbors looked out their front windows as I wrestled with the attacker. They were afraid to intervene, remaining safe behind their curtains; avoiding trouble.

At best I might expect the driver to turn the psychopath in at the next stop, but until we arrived in Salt Lake City each bus depot appeared empty of official personnel. Occasionally a lone passenger stood outside the closed buildings. They were told they could stand, or wait for the next bus. When we arrived in Salt Lake City I stayed in my seat until my seatmate hopped off the bus. After he was out of sight, one of the women sitting in front of us quickly disembarked the bus while her friend gathered their onboard luggage. The women walked over to a police officer who was standing on the loading platform. The police officer went away, and returned shortly with another officer and a security guard. Together, the three of them approached the man who had been sitting next to me. They searched his knapsack and found the knife. An officer led him away in handcuffs.

BUS 5538

Heading north from Salt Lake City to Bozeman on the Greyhound, I was glad I was still alive. My seatmate, I was sure, had been the love child of Richard Ramirez and Timothy McVeigh. After Salt Lake City I sat next to a retired admiral of the U.S. Navy. He was travelling to Bozeman. His daughter lived there with her husband and children. At first our talk was general, nothing specific or topical. I assumed there might be a political divide between us. There was still a long way to go and I wanted to avoid a harsh and uncomfortable silence.

We stopped for supper somewhere in Wyoming. It was around Yellowstone. The food was excellent in the days before Greyhound stopped only at Chubby Chicken, McDonald's and Hardee's. The retired admiral and I sat at a booth together, still carrying on with our light conversation. Suddenly he opened up. He told me he had a son who refused the induction. Instead of dodging the draft and coming to Canada the son had decided to do prison time rather than go to war. Considering the admiral's status within the military the son could have received a deferment. The son refused any preferred exemption because of the family social status. No conscientious objection. Too many poor white and black Americans did not have his options. He just didn't agree with the war. Running away had been an option, but the son went to prison for his convictions instead. The retired admiral was very proud of his son who was willing to pay a steep price for something he deeply believed. Regardless of their differences, his son would have a home to come back to when he had served his time.

BUS 6787

I think it was in Chihuahua.

I was waiting for the bus to take me north to El Paso. A young woman, one of God's special people, was panhandling very loudly. Her voice ricocheted off the walls of the cavernous depot. A rough voice, in good English with only a little bit of a Mexican accent, said,

"She should not be allowed to bother people. It is embarrassing for me to come home to Mexico and see this sort of thing."

"I don't mind. It is only a couple of pesos. Won't do me much good in Canada. What would that be, twenty-five, thirty cents."

"She should work," he continued. "I worked very hard to get everything I have."

"What do you do?"

"I own a small appliance repair shop in Dallas."

"Doing well?"

"It is difficult but I worked hard."

"How long have you lived in Dallas?"

"I came to the United States in 1984. Got a job as a laborer doing construction. I went to night school to become electrician. My family suffered much because I want to make them a better life. That is why I went to the United States, to become American. I do not want to live like a Mexican anymore. They do not have priority lined up."

"You have priorities?"

"I want American priority."

"But there must be something about Mexico that you like. You're here now."

"I come to Mexico to buy land. I grew up on a farm south of Chihuahua. My father worked very hard to make a go of it. To put food on the table, to feed mama, and my brothers and sisters."

"Who's taking care of your shop while you're here? If it's tough in Dallas, can you afford the time away?"

"My nephew looks after the shop. I sponsor him in exchange for room and board."

"Land is expensive. You must be actually doing okay. Better than you say."

"I get the land at fifty percent. Next to our farm a family lived. My father worked for the family, and on our farm. The old woman who owns the land is a widow. Never had children. She is now too old to stay on the farm, so she offered it to me, and my brother as a favor because of father. I mortgaged everything I own to make the down payment.

My house in Dallas, my shop, my family farm."

"Who looks after your farm in Mexico if you're living in Dallas?"

"My brother managed the farm, but he was killed in a car accident five years ago. Now I hire people to look after it. It has been hard. My family suffered a little more. I have my priority. An American priority to make a better life."

"You want what Americans have. Home. Car. TV."

"I've owned the same used pickup truck since 1996. I do not own a lot of things. We only owned the house few years. When we come to the United States we live in Oak Cliff, rent a nice apartment over a woman's dress store. Recently, men with big money come buying up places and increasing rents. A new kind of person come to Oak Cliff. But it is okay because we have house in the Fair Park area now. That good. Not like the Mexican. Yes, they have big fancy Dodge Rams and flat screen TVs, but they live in shit houses. What kind of priority is that? No, I work hard for all I got. It means my children have had to go without for some things. We do not have second car. My wife walks to the supermarket to buy groceries. My children work hard. They put themselves through university. They are making lives for themselves."

"You're a close family?"

"My son is a lawyer. I do not see him much. He is too

busy, he says. My daughter, I do not think she knows what she wants to do. She says, and I know she does not know what she is talking about, she wants to go back to Mexico to work as a doctor in Chiapas. She's young. She is too young to know what she wants. I'll talk her into staying. To be more like her brother. He has priority. He is American. He has an American wife. I am an American."

BUS 7430

I was travelling by bus from Thompson to Leaf Rapids. It was the end of winter. Snow still lingered everywhere up north. But it wasn't cold.

The driver and I were the only white people on the bus. He seemed to know everyone. He spoke to them in English and Cree: often in the same sentence. The bus driver would stop in the middle of nowhere for no reason, as it appeared to me, but within a few minutes people would trudge out of the bush with their Saskatoon Samsonite of green plastic bags and sacks, and board the bus. The bus would move on, only to stop again in a similarly nondescript location. This time to let people off who would disappear into the bush. The only scheduled stop between Thompson and Leaf Rapids was at Nelson House. At the junction to Nelson House an extended van waited. The bulk of the passengers disembarked and climbed into the van. A few of us remained on the bus. The bus rolled on past Notigi and on to Leaf Rapids and Lynn Lake.

What made this trip a vivid memory for me was when, on the

way from Thompson to Nelson House, a man carrying a guitar with him began to play. Very soon the bus broke out in song, singing in Cree to Johnny Cash tunes. By the time we got to Nelson House Hank Williams was filling our ears. It's moments like this I wish I wasn't so scared of singing in public.

BUS 7129

The bus from Vera Cruz pulled into Mexico City late in the afternoon. I should have spent the night there, and then taken a morning bus to Nuevo Laredo. In total our bus trip was 36 hours from Vera Cruz to Nuevo Laredo. But, no, in my stupidity, perhaps because I was anxious to get home, I took a night bus.

One hears stories about Mexico and night buses. There are as many stories about buses and banditos as there have been Big Macs eaten worldwide. I ignored the stories as we climbed aboard the Omnibus de México for the U.S. border.

The bus was quiet. The only noise was an Eddie Murphy movie dubbed in Spanish that played here and there over our heads.

Our bus took us past San Luis Potosí. A couple of hours after San Luis Potosí, the bus turned into a restaurante parking lot for a late supper break. Several buses were lined up in front of the restaurante surrounded by a sea brown earth that disappeared into flat darkness all around. Scrawny dogs sniffed the pant legs of the passengers as we disembarked.

These roadside stops are plain buildings with plain food; food made for the Mexican palate and not for the Anglos' taste buds.

It was here, at the restaurante, that the drivers were exchanged, but the change of drivers was not like it is done in Canada: a driver is waiting at a depot or at a motel along the TransCanada, in Marathon, Ontario, let us say. In the desolate terrain of Mexico, with the bus idling outside the restaurante, the driver went to what appeared to be a luggage compartment, but it was not. It was a small apartment with a bed. The replacement driver has been sleeping in the tiny apartment the whole time. The two drivers ate together, and when we left the drivers switched places.

Once again we were on the road. By now it was dark and late. I dozed off, but when I awoke we were no longer travelling on the toll road. The bus cut through the night on an undivided road. This did not seem right, but my groggy mind fumbled with the thought briefly before I dozed off again.

When I woke for the second time I found the bus was still travelling on the side road.

All those stories of banditos holding up buses, robbing the passengers, and abandoning them buck naked in the bleak landscape began to circulate in my imagination.

A woman brushed passed me and walked, jerking from side to side, to the driver. The conversation with the driver was heated. They tried to argue in whispers but were failing miserably. The two were soon screaming at each other in Spanish. The bus woke up. Passengers leaned forward. Others pressed their faces against the windows. Most passengers curled back down in their seats to grab a few more minutes or hours of sleep.

The specifics of the screaming match escaped me.

When we arrived in Nuevo Laredo, I walked across the Rio Grande to Laredo and up a block to the Greyhound depot. The woman who had argued with the bus driver was heading that way as well. She was an American, married to a Mexican, and was seeing her mother as far as Laredo, to be sure she boarded an L.A. bound bus. I told her I would make sure her mother caught her bus. Her mother was scared of everything. The woman walked back across the border to Mexico. But before she did she told me the reason for her argument with the bus driver.

On the toll road from Mexico City to Nuevo Laredo there is a tollbooth about every 100 kilometers. Sometimes the bus is pulled over and armed soldiers climb on board, and walk up and down the aisle looking for what I don't know. Toll for the buses was around 65 pesos. The drivers pay cash. It was rare for a tollbooth to accept debit of credit cards. Our midnight bus driver left the toll road and took the two-lane highway that paralleled it. The driver pocketed the cash. Between roadside restaurante and the border, there were about 8 tollbooths he was able to avoid.

He had arrived in Nuevo Laredo with 520 pesos richer.

BUS 5189

On the Greyhound, heading west. We just left Wawa behind about an hour ago.

I have felt safe on Greyhound in Canada. Travelling by bus from Mazatlan to Durango in Mexico was not as reassuring. The day before I left for Durango I was talking to a Canadian snowbird in a cantina. When I told her I was travelling to Durango by bus, she slapped her hands against her cheeks like Macaulay Culkin in Home Alone, and shrieked, "By bus?"

The bus travels across a huge mountain range. Eagles fly next to the bus at eye level. Out the window, looking down the steep slopes that appear like an abyss, one sees the mangled wreckage of cars, trucks and buses that plunged off the road.

The road is very windy and narrow. The tall cliffs obscure the road ahead, but no one seems to decrease their speed. The vehicle that honks its horn first has the right of way around a bend.

The Greyhound in Canada has no equivalent experience, but on this winter day, north of Wawa, a semi barreled through the falling snow, and as it steered around a slight bend in the road, its trailer slid into our lane. Our Greyhound driver swerved to avoid the delinquent trailer. As he did, our bus's rear slid into the oncoming lane. The driver compensated, but by now things had turned into chaos. The bus jackknifed a couple of times before it drove off the road and came to a jolting halt in a ditch, its nose buried in a snow bank. A couple of yards away a large rock, with an inuksuk perched on top of it, stood to remind us how haphazard fate can be. A blast of snow and wind knocked the inuksuk to the ground.

The driver's chest was pressed against the steering wheel, but he was fine. The passengers were shaken but in good shape as well.

It took a little more than two hours before a tow truck showed up and pulled the bus out of the ditch. An ambulance showed up shortly after. The EMTs questioned us all briefly. It was another two hours before a replacement bus arrived.

Six hours after driving off the road we headed back to

Wawa. It was twelve hours before we were on our way, heading west again.

BUS 9530

On a regional passenger bus from Winnipeg to Kansas City.
The bus pulled up to American customs. We were told to
disembark, retrieve our luggage and take it inside to
customs. The eight of us did what was asked. They gave
special attention to a Chilean who was changing buses in
Fargo for Minneapolis, where he was going to visit his sister.
He arrived in Canada in 1970 after the coup. He was now a
Canadian citizen, but customs had a hard time accepting
that. Although he had his citizenship papers and Canadian
passport, they still assumed he was trying to enter the
United States illegally. But after some persuasion, they
allowed him to enter.

American customs took a great deal of interest in a Cree
woman as well. She was travelling to visit friends in western
North Dakota. She had just returned to Canada after her
marriage to a German soldier fell apart. She had been away
from Canada for nearly ten years. Now, she was back in
Canada for six months.

In spite of her Status Card, American customs demanded

further proof she was a "North American Indian". She became irritated and argumentative.

This was post-9/11. The Jay Treaty had become a victim to heightened fear and enhanced security. The bus driver attempted to defend her, but he was reminded his job was as a bus driver and not a human rights lawyer. It was implied that he could be reported to his superiors.

The Cree woman told the driver she would be okay. It wasn't worth him getting in trouble as well.

The Cree woman was handed her luggage and began to walk to Canadian customs, to wait for a bus to take her back into Winnipeg. The bus driver asked if he could drive her to a motel on the Canadian side. It would be nearly 14 hours before the Winnipeg bus would arrive. The Americans, after some deliberations, agreed to have the driver take her to the motel. The bus turned around and crossed back into Canada. After a brief discussion with a Canadian Customs Officer, it pulled into a motel parking lot.

The bus driver took the woman's luggage and put it in the luggage compartment under the bus. He told the woman to sit at the back for a moment, and to duck down as the bus approached the Canadian/American border. The bus crossed the Canadian border. At the American border the bus was waved on through. After about 5 minutes he told the woman she could resume her seat.

South of Deloraine, where reserves on each side of the border touch, only posts divide Canada from the United States, it would be no problem for her to cross over into Canada undetected.

BUS 7145

In Salt Lake City the garbled voice on the intercom announced bus 7145 was now ready for boarding. In Salt Lake City I was required to change buses, from LA/ Chicago to Salt Lake City/Seattle. My carry-on was with me. My luggage would be transferred for me to the northbound Greyhound.

My bus was just turning onto the S 600 W to take us to I15, when I saw my suitcase on a luggage wagon parked alongside another bus. I rushed to the front of the bus to tell the driver my luggage had been left behind. He told me he had a schedule to keep, and if he failed to keep the schedule he would be penalized. Frankly, I think he was telling me I could kiss my luggage goodbye.

I was torn between being angry and sullen. A few of the passengers tried to console me, trying to lift my spirits, but I took no heed of their cheeriness. I only wanted to be sullen.

When we arrived in Bozeman I went straight to the ticket agent's counter. The agent told me, after my luggage arrived at its wrong destination, I would be contacted by Greyhound about retrieving my luggage in Fargo. Bringing it up to Winnipeg from Fargo would require another carrier who was prohibited by company policy to take unaccompanied luggage across the Canadian/American border.

In Bozeman I had to transfer to a third bus. It was about 1 or 2 in the morning when we arrived in Bozeman. The connecting bus would not arrive for another hour. There was not much to do in Bozeman at that hour but munch on snacks from vending machines, or walk around the bus depot like Joshua circling Jericho. I only circumvented the tan concrete building once when I saw, tucked in a corner, beside a Coke vending machine, my luggage, crushed like a cowering, abused animal.

BUS 2398

In 1989, travelling to California by Greyhound, the bus rolled from state to state, across bridges, through forests and over plains, and running over tumbleweed that jaywalked across the interstate. In 1989 one could smoke in the rear of the buses (and, boy, did we smoke), if the state travelling through permitted smoking on buses. So our cigarette habit would hopscotch across the western U.S. of A. I can no longer recall the three states involved (might have been Arizona, Nevada and California), but we were travelling in a no-smoking state and approaching one that permitted smoking. About a mile before the border the driver announced we were soon be passing through a small corner of a smoking state, "If you got 'em, smoke 'em. But you will have only 5 minutes to smoke before we enter California where you will need to butt 'em."

All the smokers had their cigarettes hanging out of their mouths, with lighters or matches at the ready.

Smoking state. Click, scratch, puff, puff, puff. Out.

When the bus pulled over for a break, to stretch our legs, get a coffee or purchase another sugar donut, the passengers poured out of the bus gasping for oxygen, including the smokers.

The driver got a coffee, found a little shade, and lit up a cigarette.

In fifteen minutes we were on our way again. Cigarettes could wait until we got to L.A.

BUS 5612

I have two daughters.

Many years ago

When the oldest was about two years old

I took her by bus to see her grandmother in Selkirk.

A tall East African immigrant boarded the bus

And sat directly behind us.

My daughter stared and stared at him.

Could not take her eyes off of him.

I tried to get her to sit down

But she would immediately stand and stare at him again.

I apologized if she was causing any discomfort.

As he stood

To get off the bus at the Middlechurch stop,

He said to me,

"She hasn't seen many of us,

Has she?"

BUS 2014

They named a junction after him. Some of the older folks thought that was a dumb idea, since he probably deserved what was coming to him. But their opinion was based on rumor, and rumors that, in time, and repeated enough, became fact.

He loved motor racing. There was not a motor race in California he hadn't competed in. He found motor racing liberating. His spirit and body became exempt in this world when he was behind the wheel of a fast car.

His pride and joy were his Triumph Tiger T110 and his Porsche 356.

He had been scheduled for a racing event in Salinas, California on Sunday. Following him that Saturday afternoon had been a Hollywood real estate executive, a photographer from an international men's magazine, and a German car mechanic. Unable to keep up with him, they'd lost sight of the Porsche. Around 3:30 pm that afternoon he was ticketed for speeding. He was clocked in at 135 miles per hour.

He continued his drive to Salinas. He drove the speed limit for about fifteen minutes before he couldn't stand it anymore. He pushed the pedal to the metal. His heart raced with the car.

At the intersection of 101 and I98, he crashed his Porsche into the rear end of a regional passenger bus that was making a right hand turn onto 101. The Porsche bounced across the pavement and ended up at the side of the highway. The Porsche was broken into pieces, and so was he. His neck snapped in two and he died instantly. The passengers of the bus were only shaken up a little. Except for a teen who had a bloody nose, but he suffered from Thrombocytopenia, so, it was uncertain if the accident had been the cause of the bleeding nose or not.

News of his death spread quickly across the country. There wasn't an ear in America that had not heard of his death before the day was through. Ten years later a folk singer from Ohio would write a song about him.

While he was found to be at fault for the accident, travelling beyond the speed limit, many of his fans blamed the driver of the regional bus. The bus driver received death threats. The bus driver had to go into hiding. A year passed. The driver of the bus believed enough time had passed and felt he could move about freely. On a late Sunday afternoon, while his wife was checking on the pot roast in the oven, he was fetching water from the pump. A crack blasted the air apart. The bus driver slumped, his body folding over the trough, his head was submerged.

The cows didn't seem to mind.

BUS 4655

Before I arrived in Barstow I had already heard Harry
Partch's Barstow: Eight Hitchhiker Inscriptions from a
Highway Railing at Barstow, California.

73

Blackwell. Age nineteen. Brown eyes, brown hair. Oh, but I'm considered pretty. Here is where I live: One-eighteen East Ventura Street, Las Vegas, Nevada. Object: matrimony.

Number Four
Dear Marie, a very good idea you have there. I too am on the lookout for a suitable mate. My description . . .

Number Five
Possible rides: January sixteenth, fifty-eight. January seventeenth, seventy-six. January eighteenth, nineteen. January nineteenth, six. January twentieth, eleven. To hell with it -- I'm going to walk!

Barstow was reaching mythological levels in my imagination. I walked and drove around Barstow in a rental car to see if I could find similar inscriptions of hobos and hitchhikers. It was unbearably hot. And all around me as far as the eye could see, tan. Just tan.

All I found was:

Why must I be a teenager in love?

Mutate now. Avoid the post-bomb rush.

You all tend to tell us we are not wanted here. I will remember that next time I med-vac your ass.

Marry me Trish.

If your back is against the wall turn around and write on it.

For a good BJ call Shirley at 442-818-6583.

I wanted to kill more Congs but the army wouldn't let me.

Go home if you don't like it.

I wish I knew where home was but I'm lost.

Trish, I love you. True love.

I returned the rental car. Took a taxi to the bus depot and waited in the coffee shop. Had two bad coffees and an egg salad sandwich. Waited for the westward bound Greyhound bus. Me and several Mexicans and an old man with no teeth.

Grant Guy is a Winnipeg (Canada) playwright, theatre director, poet and writer. For sixteen years Grant was the artistic director of Adhere And Deny. Currently he holds that position with Two Horses of Paladin. *Bus Stop Bus Stop* is Grant's second collection of stories, following the 2015 release of *On The Bright Side of Down*. Grant's poetry and short stories have appeared in numerous journals and magazines in Canada and the United States.

The Artist—

Shawn Jordan is an interdisciplinary artist living on the windswept Canadian prairies. Through her work - drawing, painting, video, and performance - she explores "the stories we tell ourselves in out heads", shifting perceptions, and other nonsense.

8043

43368193R00051